LINKING
Math and
techNoLogy

grade 5

Creative Publications®

This book is based on the MathLand series, which was
written by Linda Charles, Micaelia Randolph Brummett,
Heather McDonald, and Joan Westley.

Writer: Lynn Sanchez
Project Editor: Nora Sweeny
Classroom Coordinator: Ema Arcellana

Creative Director: Ken Shue
Art Director: Janice Kawamoto
Cover Illustration: David Broad
Production Coordinator: Ed Lazar
Production Services: Morgan-Cain & Associates

©1995 Creative Publications
1300 Villa Street
Mountain View, CA 94041

Printed in the United States of America.
ISBN: 1-56107-832-8
1 2 3 4 5 6 7 8 9 10 99 98 97 96 95

contents

Your guide to Linking Math and Technology

- **You can create a mathematical and technology-rich environment for students.**

  In this environment students are encouraged to think, invent, investigate, and make connections using the computer. As a guide and facilitator, you can ask questions or propose challenges, and then stand back, observe, and listen.

- **The investigations in this book invite a diversity of approaches.**

  Different ways of thinking are expected and encouraged. Every child will bring something different and unique to the experience and gain something different from the experience.

- **Students use blank paper for these investigations.**

  Students can approach the tasks at their own level and think about it in their own way—there's room for different levels of prior knowledge, different languages, and all kinds of thinking. Authentic work produced by students who tested the program is featured throughout the book.

- **Manipulative materials are essential for mathematical understanding.**

  Students use manipulative models to enhance their understandings of mathematical concepts. The kit provided with this book has appropriate materials for the investigations.

- **Computers help students see mathematical ideas in a new light.**

  By using computers, students can develop new strategies for solving mathematical problems. They may notice that the computer provides a more accurate way of making a graph, or that the changing data that is reflected quickly on the screen graph shows how the pattern holds, or that convincing someone of their ideas may be easier when the elements of animation and sound and color are added.

- **Computers become a new tool for clarifying and deepening understandings of mathematical ideas.**

  The computer is much more than just an electronic paper and pencil. As the students develop the skills necessary to become proficient with these new tools, the results can be astounding—what the students create using these programs are highly sophisticated projects. But the students also learn that what the computer produces is the direct result of their creativity, thoughtfulness, and understanding of the mathematical concepts.

The thoughtful and creative use of technology can greatly improve both the quality of the curriculum and the quality of children's learning. Integrating calculators and computers into school mathematics programs is critical in meeting the goals of a redefined curriculum.

National Council of Teachers of Mathematics
Curriculum and Evaluation Standards for School Mathematics

How is Linking Math and Technology organized?

This book is organized into ten investigations. These in-depth investigations are designed to let you know what to do each step of the way.

These NCTM strands are integrated throughout the investigations:

- **Number relations**
- **Logic and language**
- **Probability and statistics**
- **Patterns and functions**
- **Data analysis**

- **Measurement**
- **Discrete mathematics**
- **Geometry and visual thinking**
- **Algebra**

In these investigations, students are doing real math all the time.

- **They produce original reports and projects.**
- **They organize their material in ways that make sense to them.**
- **Their solutions reflect their personal understandings.**
- **They use manipulatives to make learning real.**
- **Their work together promotes cooperation and results in richer thinking.**

How can i integrate these investigations in my curriculum?

Use these investigations to connect math and computers in the classroom as supplements or extensions to your regular mathematics curriculum. The investigations can enhance other curriculum areas as well—social studies, art, language arts, science, and so on. These ten investigations correlate with units in the MathLand series (see the chart on page 1), but they may be used in any order you choose to augment your curriculum. Once the students have worked through the tutorials and are familiar with the software, they are knowledgeable enough to do the investigations in any order you specify.

What materials will i need to do the investigations?

The **Classroom Manipulatives Kit** provides plenty of materials for the whole class and is used for the curriculum-based initiating activity. It includes:

- **Pattern Blocks**
- **Base Ten Blocks**
- **3-oz. Portion Cups**
- **1-oz. Portion Cups**
- **Set of Measuring Cups**
- **Vinyl Inch/Metric Rulers**
- **Rainbow Cubes**
- **Polygon Tiles and Definition Cards**

Other materials you will need:

- **blank paper (full, half, and quarter sheets)**
- **pencils, crayons, markers**
- **paste or glue sticks**
- **tape**
- **stapler**
- **calculators**

How are these investigations organized?

Each four-page investigation is made up of the components listed below. These components are designed so that you can cover each investigation easily, using numbered guidelines and step-by-step computer procedures.

WHAT IS THIS INVESTIGATION ABOUT?

You'll find a brief overview and unifying mathematical ideas covered in the investigation.

PLANNING FOR THE INVESTIGATION

You'll see a list of the materials needed for the investigation—manipulatives, paper, supplies, and preparation—as well as what software you'll use.

BEFORE THE INVESTIGATION

You'll complete a brief whole-class activity that triggers student thinking before you begin the investigation.

INITIATING THE INVESTIGATION

These numbered guidelines provide you with a step-by-step process to follow, with clear instructions for both you and your students. Words in bold italic are "teacher talk," and helpful hints for you are boxed in the margin. Diagrams and sample student work show what the students will be doing at various stages in the investigation.

INTEGRATING SOFTWARE INTO THE INVESTIGATION

These numbered instructions suggest how you might work with the students through the computer extension, with step-by-step computer procedures and shortcuts listed in the left margin. Sample student work provides a preview of what you can expect from your own students.

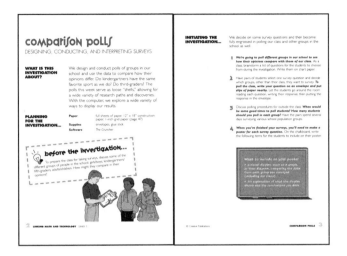

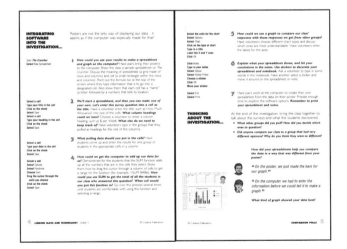

THINKING ABOUT THE INVESTIGATION

Here is your chance to learn from the children themselves what knowledge they have created from their work. There are sample assessment questions, and the dialog box shows how real students responded to the investigation.

How should i organize my class for these investigations?

The majority of these investigations are designed for pairs or groups of four students, with each child assigned a task—observer, director, operator, and checker; or writer, illustrator, sound recorder, and editor. Students should rotate roles each time they use the computer. Encourage students to teach one another what they have learned from previous computer experience or the tutorials. Teacher assistants, parent volunteers, and upper-grade students can also be trained to become computer experts. Give the class guidelines for using the computers: when they may use them, how to name their files, and when they can print or play back their work.

How long do these investigations take?

In a classroom with several computers, it may be possible for the class to complete each investigation over a few days. In a classroom where only one computer is available, you may want to complete **Initiating the Investigation** with the entire class, and then let groups of students complete the computer extension as time allows (over a period of days or weeks). Whether your class has one computer or many, **Thinking About the Investigation** is a good time to gather students together after they have all completed the investigation, to view each other's projects and to assess what was learned from the process.

What Software Have You Developed for My Classroom?

The two software tools for the intermediate grades are *The Cruncher* and *The Multimedia Workshop*. Both packages are available for the Macintosh or Windows, in English or Spanish, for single or multiple users.

The Cruncher, by Davidson and Associates, Inc., gives students in the intermediate grades the power to create projects that compute, graph, and teach math concepts in an exciting way. From their data, students can visualize and analyze their results with pie and scatter charts and bar and line graphs. Tutorials show each step of the formulas they use, and a powerful text-to-speech feature allows students to listen to words or numbers in their documents. The notebook and a library of colorful stickers, illustrations, and animation adds to the discourse of their work. *The Cruncher* includes three modules: the **Spreadsheet, Tutorials,** and **Projects**. The **Spreadsheet** has all the features students would expect to find in a professional spreadsheet program: mathematical operators, functions, and graphing. The **Tutorials** introduce the elements of spreadsheets and special features of *The Cruncher* in step-by-step, self-guided sequences. The **Projects** provide investigative situations with illustrated text and preformatted spreadsheets to give students more hands-on experience with the mathematical concepts.

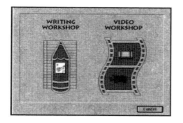

The Multimedia Workshop, by Davidson and Associates, Inc., allows students to plan, develop, and create documents and multimedia presentations. *The Multimedia Workshop* includes immense libraries of photographs, illustrations, sounds, and video clips on CD-ROM. Three modules that make up this sophisticated program are the **Writing Workshop, Paint Workshop**, and **Video Workshop**. The **Writing Workshop** is an elaborate word processing program that includes a spell-checker, thesaurus, and document templates. The **Paint Workshop** is a full-featured paint program. In it, photographs and clip art can be modified and backgrounds can be created with the many tools in the toolbox. The original art work created in the **Paint Workshop** can be printed directly or used in the students' published documents and video presentations. Students can use their art and text to create sophisticated multimedia presentations in the **Video Workshop.**

How can i get a running start with the software?

You can become familiar with the software by reading the user manuals, but spending actual "hands-on" time with the software is the fastest way. The tutorials provide a 30-minute overview of all the features you'll need for the investigations. The manuals also provide some useful tips on how to set up the software to make it easier for the students to use. Here are some suggestions:

- **Make computer folders or directories to hold the documents and files that the students create.**
- **Set preferences and defaults for the font, type size, sound, and so on that are appropriate for your students.**
- **Arrange and simplify the windows on the screen.**
- **Disable functions that are unnecessary.**

How should i introduce the software to the students?

It is important to set aside some time, especially in the beginning, so the students can freely explore the software. Give them a tour of the tutorials and templates. Before each investigation, review the menus, buttons, actions (especially **SAVE**), and folder locations so students can find their work when they need to! You may find it helpful to review software-specific terminology—*icons, files*, and *save,* for example—and demonstrate pertinent features, too.

is the software easy to use?

The ten investigations here have been specially designed for use with these two software packages. And the software has been tested and used by thousands of children. If you have problems with the software, you may find the online help menus and troubleshooting tips in the manuals helpful. If you have problems that can't be solved by referring to the manuals or using the online help menus, call the toll-free customer support numbers listed in the manuals.

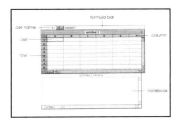

PERFORMANCE TIPS FOR *THE CRUNCHER*

- Remember that all formulas must begin with an equal sign.
- ***The Cruncher*** calculates so quickly that students may miss the operation. When you demonstrate formulas or functions, click between the data and **Show** several times so they can see what is happening to the data within the cell.
- To create a chart, you must choose columns that are adjacent to one another.

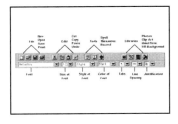

PERFORMANCE TIPS FOR *THE MULTIMEDIA WORKSHOP*

- ***The Multimedia Workshop*** produces several types of documents. Review with students how to recognize documents from the **Libraries**, **Writing Workshop**, **Scene Maker**, and **Sequencer**, and set up a system for project folders.
- To prevent crashes and error messages, set the memory to the size recommended by the developer.

Let's peek into our Linking Math and Technology classroom.

DURING THE MATH INVESTIGATION

The students use same-shape Pattern Blocks to "grow" polygons. They identify patterns in the shapes they've built, and show the patterns they've discovered on grid paper. The students use their discoveries to predict what will happen if their polygons continue to grow.

Students use the Pattern Blocks to build bigger and bigger polygons. When they run out of blocks, the students transfer their growing shapes onto grid paper.

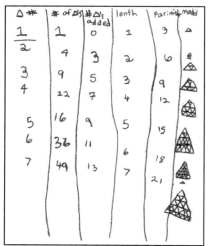

As they add polygons, they keep track of the perimeter and number of polygons used. They record the data and begin to see some patterns in the numbers.

△ #	# of △s	# △'s added	lenth	Parimi made	
1/2	1	0	1	3	△
	4	3	2	6	
3	9	5	3	9	
4	12	7	4	12	
5	16	9	5	15	
6	36	11	6	18	
7	49	13	7	21	

these students are linking the cruncher with their growing shapes.

DURING THE TECHNOLOGY EXTENSION

The patterns are reinforced when the students use formulas in *The Cruncher* that agree with modeling and paper-and-pencil work. The spreadsheet results are blockbusters!

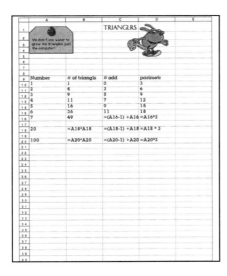

After students review the elements of the spreadsheet (cells, rows, columns, formula bar), they enter their data: the number of blocks in the shape and the number of blocks added to the last shape. Students try to find formulas that explain the patterns for area, perimeter, and number of polygons added in the shapes they built. They enter the formulas in "spreadsheet-ese"—by using the cell name and the asterisk as the multiplication sign.

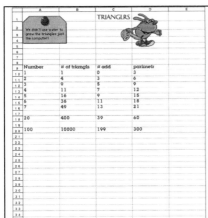

The results on their spreadsheets convince them that the patterns they discovered will work even for shapes too big for their grid paper—even for triangle 100!

> **Letter from a Teacher**
> This investigation was the first one I chose to do using *The Cruncher.* The step-by-step format of the lesson was so straightforward that I had no problems planning it or walking my students through the process. My students enjoyed the hands-on building and paper-and-pencil work, but they were amazed that they could take a pattern and create a formula on the spreadsheet that would work for every shape, no matter how large.

Let's peek into our Linking Math and technology classroom.

DURING THE MATH INVESTIGATION

Students have a hands-on experience with a really large number—one million! How many cups of birdseed does it take to make a million? After some brainstorming, the students discover some nifty shortcuts to count the birdseed. And they write about their methods so they don't forget.

Students spend some time making a plan to find out how many cups it will take to hold a million birdseeds. Counting by ones and fives would take forever—are there other ways to count faster?

One Million

We counted out seeds and put them into a cup. It took 336 seeds to fill it. Then we tried to figer out how many cups it takes to get to 1,000,000. We used a calcalator. We did 1000000 ÷ 336 and got 2976.1904. So we would have to put out 2976 cups. That would take a <u>long</u> time.

Students discover that finding how many seeds are in one cup of seeds is a good way to begin. And their powers of estimation are aided by the calculator! Students keep track of their thinking by drawing and writing about what they know about one million.

these students are linking the multimedia workshop with birdseed by the million.

DURING THE TECHNOLOGY EXTENSION

Students plan how they can explain all that they know about one million to their third-grade buddies. They make multimedia presentations that entertain and inform their buddies using all the high-tech tools available in *The Multimedia Workshop.*

We counted out seeds and put them into a cup. It took 336 seeds to fill it.

Students start with the tools that appeal to them: those who like to draw create illustrations in the **Paint Workshop**. Others write about what they discovered in the **Writing Workshop.** And others preview clip art and movies in the **Libraries**, and use them to build their scenes.

Then we tried to figer out how many cups it takes to get to 1,000,000. We used a calcalator. We did 1000000 ÷ 336 and got 2976.19.

Once their scenes are complete, the students add sounds or personally narrate their presentations. They also experiment with the transitions—their presentations look more and more professional. The students finish up their presentations and get ready to play them for the third-graders. Later, they copy their presentations onto videotape to share with family members at home.

Letter from a Teacher

When I first read this investigation, I had my doubts—all those birdseeds and complicated computer instructions?! The students worked with the seeds so carefully yet enthusiastically that I was surprised and encouraged. And as I worked through the computer directions, I realized they were easy to follow—it's a one-step-at-a-time process. There were several students in my classes who were very comfortable with the software, and they helped the whole class. When we were ready to show the presentations, I brought in a big monitor so everyone could enjoy their very professional work.

Hardware requirements

To run **THE CRUNCHER,** you will need

For the Macintosh environment:
- Mac Classic or above
- 4 MB or more with 2 MB free RAM
- 13 MB on hard disk
- System 7.0 or higher
- Printer (highly recommended)

For the PC environment:
- IBM Compatible
- 80386 16 MHz or better
- 4 MB RAM
- 12 MB on hard disk
- Windows 3.1 or higher
- Sound card (recommended)
- Printer (highly recommended)

To run **THE MULTIMEDIA WORKSHOP,** you will need

For the Macintosh environment:
- LC or above
- 4 MB or more RAM for 256 colors; 8 MB or more for Thousands of Colors
- 8 MB on hard disk
- System 7.0 or higher
- CD-ROM Drive (highly recommended)
- Printer (highly recommended)
- Microphone (highly recommended)

For the PC environment:
- IBM Compatible
- 80486 25 MHz or better
- 4 MB minimum RAM (8 MB recommended)
- 20 MB on hard disk
- CD-ROM Drive (highly recommended)
- Windows 3.1 or higher
- Sound card (required)
- Printer (highly recommended)
- Microphone (highly recommended)

key mathematical ideas covered

The ten investigations in this book correlate with the key mathematical ideas and projects in the MathLand series listed below.

Investigation	MathLand Project	Key Mathematical Ideas
Comparison Polls	**Unit 1/Week 2**	Data Analysis Patterns Logical Thinking
Growing Shapes	**Unit 2/Week 1**	Patterns Functions Geometry Visual Thinking Logical Thinking
Ancient Algorithms	**Unit 3/Week 2**	Number Relations Patterns Visual Thinking
Category Cards	**Unit 4/Week 1**	Logic Algebra Patterns
Birdseed by the Million	**Unit 5/Week 2**	Number Relations Logical Thinking
Creating Containers	**Unit 6/Week 2**	Measurement Visual Thinking Logical Thinking Discrete Math
Boxes in Boxes	**Unit 7/Week 4**	Number Relations Measurement Patterns Visual Thinking
Tessellation Art	**Unit 8/Week 4**	Geometry Visual Thinking Patterns
Number Systems Expo	**Unit 9/Week 4**	Number Relations Patterns Logical Thinking
Predictions	**Unit 10/Week 1**	Probability Statistics Logical Thinking

comparison polls

DESIGNING, CONDUCTING, AND INTERPRETING SURVEYS

WHAT IS THIS INVESTIGATION ABOUT?

We design and conduct polls of groups in our school and use the data to compare how their opinions differ. Do kindergartners have the same favorite sport as we do? Do third-graders? The polls this week serve as loose "shells," allowing for a wide variety of research paths and discoveries. With the computer, we explore a wide variety of ways to display our results.

PLANNING FOR THE INVESTIGATION...

Paper	full sheets of paper, 12" x 18" construction paper, 1-inch grid paper (page 47)
Supplies	envelopes, glue stick
Software	*The Cruncher*

before the investigation...

To prepare the class for taking surveys, discuss some of the different groups of people in the school: girls/boys; kindergartners/fifth-graders; adults/children. How might they compare in their opinions?

INITIATING THE INVESTIGATION...

We decide on some survey questions and then become fully engrossed in polling our class and other groups in the school as well.

1. *We're going to poll different groups in our school to see how their opinions compare with those of our class.* As a class, brainstorm a list of questions for the students to choose from during the investigation. Write them on chart paper.

2. Have pairs of students select one survey question and decide which groups, other than their class, they want to survey. *To poll the class, write your question on an envelope and put slips of paper nearby.* Let the students go around the room reading each question, writing their response, then putting the response in the envelope.

3. Discuss polling procedures for outside the class. *When would be some good times to poll students? How many students should you poll in each group?* Have the pairs spend several days surveying various school population groups.

4. *When you've finished your surveys, you'll need to make a poster for each survey question.* On the chalkboard, write the following items for the students to include on their poster.

> **What to include on your poster**
>
> • a visual display, such as a graph, or Venn diagram, comparing the data from each group you surveyed (including our class)
>
> • An explanation of what the display shows and the conclusions you drew

INTEGRATING SOFTWARE INTO THE INVESTIGATION...

Posters are not the only way of displaying our data...it seems as if the computer was especially made for that!

Open *The Cruncher*
Select New Spreadsheet

1 *How could you use your results to make a spreadsheet and graph on the computer?* Have pairs bring their posters to the computer. Show the class a sample spreadsheet on *The Cruncher*. Discuss the meaning of *spreadsheet* (a grid made of rows and columns) and *cell* (a small rectangle within the rows and columns). Point out the *formula bar* at the top of the screen where they type information that is to go into a designated cell. Also show them that each cell has a "name" (a letter followed by a number) that tells its location.

Select a cell
Type your title in the cell
Click on the check
Select Save
Select a cell
Type your heading in the cell
Click on the check
Select Save

2 *We'll start a spreadsheet, and then you can make one of your own. Let's enter this survey question into a cell as the title.* Have a volunteer enter the title, such as How Much Allowance? into one of the cells. *What column headings could we have?* Choose a volunteer to enter a column heading, such as $ per Week. *What else do we need to keep track of?* Have volunteers type in the groups that they polled as headings for the rest of the columns.

Select a cell
Type your data in the cell
Click on the check
Select Save

3 *What polling data should you put in the cells?* Have students come up and enter the results for one group of students in the appropriate cells in a column.

Select a cell
Select Options
Select Functions
Choose Sum
Drag the cursor through the cells you choose
Click on the check
Select Save

4 *How could we get the computer to add up our data for us?* Demonstrate for the students that the SUM function adds up all the numbers that are in the cells they select. Show them how to drag the cursor through a column of cells to get a range for the function (for example, =SUM B4:B6). *How could you use SUM to get the total of all the students in our class who answered this question? What cell would you put this function in?* Go over this process several times until students are comfortable with using the function and selecting a range.

Select the cells for the chart
Select Options
Select Chart
Click on the type of chart
Type in a title
Label the X and Y axes
Click OK

Click Notes
Type in your notes
Select Option
Select Sticker Picker
Choose a sticker
Click OK
Move your sticker

Select File
Select Print

THINKING ABOUT THE INVESTIGATION...

5 *How could we use a graph to compare our class' responses with those responses we got from other groups?* Have volunteers choose different chart types and discuss which ones are most understandable. Have volunteers enter the labels for the axes.

6 *Explain what your spreadsheet shows, and list your conclusions in the notes. Use stickers to decorate your spreadsheet and notebook.* Ask a volunteer to type in some words in the notebook. Have another select a sticker and move it around on the spreadsheet or note.

7 Have pairs work at the computer to create their own spreadsheet from the data on their poster. Provide enough time to explore the software options. *Remember to print your spreadsheet and notes.*

At the end of the investigation, bring the class together to talk about the surveys and what the students discovered.

- *What other groups did you poll? How did you decide which ones to question?*
- *Did anyone compare our class to a group that had very different opinions? Why do you think they were so different?*

How did your spreadsheets help you compare the data in a way that was different from your poster?

" *On the poster, we just made the bars for our graph.* "

" *On the computer we had to enter the information before we could tell it to make a graph.* "

What kind of graph showed your data best?

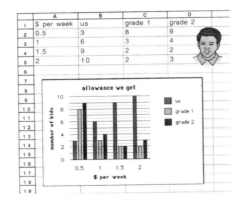

growing shapes
INVESTIGATING PATTERNS WITH PATTERN BLOCKS

WHAT IS THIS INVESTIGATION ABOUT?

Recognizing patterns and using them to predict is an important mathematical strategy. We build geometric shapes to explore and identify patterns among different sizes of one shape and then among different shapes. We learn to show these patterns on the computer in a way that seems logical to us.

PLANNING FOR THE INVESTIGATION...

Manipulatives Kit	*For each pair:* Pattern Blocks (14 green, red, blue, and tan blocks; 7 orange and yellow blocks)
Paper	chart paper; full sheets of paper; 1-inch grid paper (page 47), Triangle grid paper (page 48)
Supplies	calculators, colored marking pens
Software	*The Cruncher*
Preparation	Make a copy of Growing Shapes Explorations (page 42) for each pair.

before the investigation...

We're going to build larger and larger squares and try to find a pattern. Show the students a square Pattern Block. **This is the smallest square. How many blocks does it use?** Indicate one side. **We'll call this length 1. How long is each side of our square?** Have students work in pairs to build larger and larger squares. **Use grid paper when you run out of squares and keep a record of the patterns you see.**

INITIATING THE INVESTIGATION...

We grow Pattern Block shapes and make recordings of what we see. Then we make predictions from the patterns we find.

1 Have the students look at their Pattern Block recording. **What patterns do you see in these squares you've made ?** On the chalkboard, list the students' ideas. Suggest these ideas for exploration if they don't occur to the students: total number of blocks in each square, side length of each square, perimeter of each square, and number of blocks you add each time (number of blocks larger this square is than the last). On chart paper, create a table to organize the data. Have volunteers fill in the data and discuss the patterns that students found.

2 *Now you are ready to explore growing shapes patterns with some other shapes in our Pattern Blocks set.* Distribute and discuss the Growing Shapes Explorations with the class. Have pairs explore the ideas that interest them.

3 When students have finished their recordings, gather the class together so the students can discuss their findings. **Do we see the same patterns with other shapes as we saw with squares? Do the patterns continue as the shapes get larger? Mathematicians call numbers like 1, 4, 9, and 16 "square numbers." Any ideas why?**

> For the square, triangle, and rhombus, it is easiest to build the shapes first and then record the patterns. The trapezoids can be tricky. Encourage students to build them by using the patterns they've developed from squares and triangles. Hexagons don't seem to follow the pattern because they can't be made from hexagons. Tell students that when they build the second hexagon from a combination of hexagons and other blocks, the pattern is consistent if they count those other blocks in terms of hexagons.

Square number	Model	Number of blocks needed	Number of blocks added to last square	Length of a side	Perimeter
1	□	1	1	1	4
2	⊞	4	3	2	8
3	▦	9	5	3	12
4	▦	16	7	4	16
5					

INTEGRATING SOFTWARE INTO THE INVESTIGATION...

We organize our data onto spreadsheets. We explain what we found out with this high-tech assistance.

Open *The Cruncher*
Select New Spreadsheet

1 *We'll use the information you got from Growing Shapes Explorations to make spreadsheets on the computer. Let's start one together, and then you can create your own.* Discuss with the students the meaning of a *spreadsheet* (a grid made of rows and columns) and *cell* (a small rectangle within the rows and columns). Show them a sample on *The Cruncher.* Point out the formula bar at the top of the screen, which is where they type information that is to go into a designated cell.

Select a cell
Type your title in the cell
Select Save
Select a cell
Type your heading in the cell
Select Save

2 *Let's do one for squares. What do you think would be a good title to enter into a cell?* Growing Squares is one example. *What column headings could you enter in your spreadsheet?* Call on a volunteer to enter headings, such as square number, number of blocks, number added, length of side, and perimeter.

Select a cell
Type your data in the cell
Select Save

3 *How could we enter our data for the squares in the first two columns?* Pick volunteers to type the numbers into the appropriate cells in these columns.

Select a cell
Type in an equal sign
Type in your formula
Click on the check
Select Save

4 *What formulas could you use to put data in the next column? Use your recording to help you.* Students might enjoy the challenge of figuring out how to count by odd numbers in the "number added" column, for example (= number in cell above +2). Go through several cells to demonstrate the use of the formula.

	A	B	C	D	E
1			TRIANGLRS		
2	We didn't use water to grow the triangles just the computer!				
3					
4					
5					
6					
7					
8					
9	Number	# of triangls	# add	parimetr	
10	1	1	0	3	
11	2	4	3	6	
12	3	9	5	9	
13	4	11	7	12	

Click Notes
Type in your notes
Select Option
Select Sticker Picker
Choose a sticker
Click OK
Move your sticker

Select File
Select Print

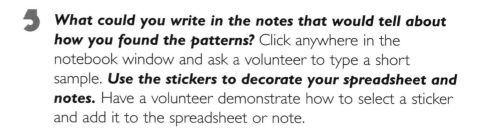

What could you write in the notes that would tell about how you found the patterns? Click anywhere in the notebook window and ask a volunteer to type a short sample. **Use the stickers to decorate your spreadsheet and notes.** Have a volunteer demonstrate how to select a sticker and add it to the spreadsheet or note.

Have pairs work at the computer to make their own spreadsheet. **Before you start, pick a shape and think about the data you want to put into the columns and rows. Make sure it would tell someone what the shape is and what the patterns are. Remember to print your spreadsheet and notes. Add color to them if you'd like.** Allow the students time to explore the software options.

THINKING ABOUT THE INVESTIGATION...

Toward the end of the investigation, have the students bring their spreadsheets to the discussion area to share with the class.

- **How were your patterns revealed on the spreadsheet?**
- **If you were to change your spreadsheet, what would you do differently?**

Did anyone use formulas in the spreadsheet to fill in the cells?

" I used a multiplication formula to get how many blocks were needed. Because we knew from our table that you multiplied the first number by itself. **"**

" I tried to do that but it took a long time. It was faster to do it in my head. **"**

Did anyone use a formula to find the perimeter?

Ancient Algorithms
INVESTIGATING ALTERNATIVE METHODS OF MULTIPLICATION

WHAT IS THIS INVESTIGATION ABOUT?

We explore ancient multiplication algorithms that show us that there has always been more than one way to get the correct answer. Our mathematical power and technical acuity is increased as we choose one of these algorithms to present as a video.

PLANNING FOR THE INVESTIGATION...

Manipulatives Kit *For each pair:*
Base Ten Blocks (2 hundreds, 10 tens, 20 ones)

Paper full sheets of paper

Supplies calculators

Software *The Multimedia Workshop*

Preparation Make one copy of the Russian Peasant Multiplication algorithm, the Egyptian Multiplication algorithm, and Lattice Multiplication algorithm (pages 43-44) for each pair.

before the investigation...

Introduce Base Ten Blocks as one strategy for solving two-digit multiplication problems. On the board, write the equation 3 × 4 = 12. **Three rows of 4 equals 12.** Encourage groups of four to use Base Ten Blocks to build a rectangle with 3 rows of 4 blocks. Draw the solution on the board. Continue this with more challenging problems: 10 × 10, 12 × 13, and so on, using the "rows of" language.

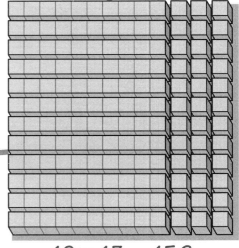

12 x 13 = 156

INITIATING THE INVESTIGATION...

Investigating ancient algorithms is fun and challenging! They even make us think about some of the strategies we use…

▶ In Egypt, the basic arithmetic operation was addition—our operation of multiplication was first performed through successive doubling. India seems to be where lattice multiplication began; it was carried to China and Arabia. Used in Italy by the fourteenth and fifteenth centuries, it was called *gelosia* because it resembled the window gratings in Venice.

▶ Presenting these different problem-solving strategies—manipulatives, algorithms, and calculators—further reinforces the idea that there are many ways to solve an arithmetic problem. When solving problems, it is important for students to find strategies that make sense to them, rather than merely memorizing one way to do it.

1. *Since the beginning of time, people have been trying to invent quick ways (or short cuts) of figuring out arithmetic problems.* Hand out the sheets on Russian, Egyptian, and lattice multiplication. You may want to discuss the historical significance of these algorithms with the class. Some students may be interested in researching this on their own.

2. As students work with their partners and investigate these ancient algorithms, have them try the same multiplication problems using the Base Ten Blocks. Remind them to use the "rows of" language. Provide calculators for students to check their work.

3. After the students have worked through the algorithms, bring the class together for a discussion. *What problems did you solve using these algorithms? Did you get the correct answer? How do you know? Which of these methods of multiplying was the most efficient? Tell why you think so.*

4. *Decide which ancient algorithm you prefer.* Have students work with their partner and choose together which algorithm they will be making into a video.

INTEGRATING SOFTWARE INTO THE INVESTIGATION...

From the ancient world to the high-tech world—what a leap, but we're up for the challenge!

Open **The Multimedia Workshop**
Select Video Workshop Scene
  Maker
Open Libraries
Choose Clip Art **or** Photographs
Import **your illustration**
Select a background
Type in your text
Save **your scene**

Select Paint Workshop
Create your illustration
Save **your illustration**
Select Video Workshop Scene
  Maker
Import **your illustration**
Save **your scene**

Select Video Workshop Sequencer
Click on the first box on the
  video track
Import **your scene**
Select a transition
Place your transition
Save **your movie**

1 *Let's make a video presentation of the algorithm you chose. Start by making a scene—all videos are just a series of scenes.* Some students may want to begin with illustrations from the Libraries.

2 Other students may prefer to create their own illustrations in the Paint Workshop. *Let's show how we could solve this algorithm in another scene.* Remind students of the variety of tools and features available to explain their thinking. Tell the students they can make as many scenes as they want to describe how they solved the problem using the algorithm.

3 After the students have made several scenes, they're ready to make a movie. *You can put all your scenes together to make a presentation.* Have students demonstrate for the class how to place several scenes and transitions to remind others of the various steps.

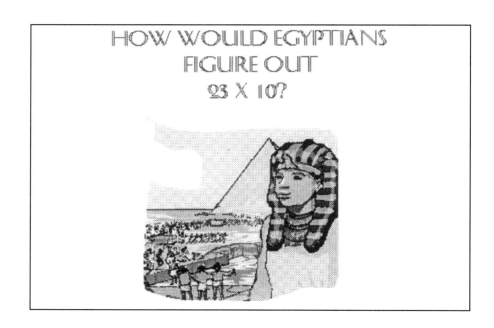

Click on the soundtrack
Open Libraries
Open Sound
Select some sound or music
Save **your movie**

Open Playback
Click Save & Play
Select Auto Play

THINKING ABOUT THE INVESTIGATION...

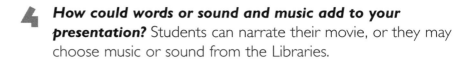

4 *How could words or sound and music add to your presentation?* Students can narrate their movie, or they may choose music or sound from the Libraries.

5 *Now we are ready to watch our creations!* As the pairs finish their investigations, set aside some time for them to give their video presentations to the class.

After all the presentations have been viewed, gather the class together so they can discuss their findings.

- *How did you organize your presentation?*
- *How did you show the algorithm on your presentation?*

How would you show how to use Base Ten Blocks to solve multiplication problems?

" *I would draw the rows of ones and the squares of hundreds.* "

" *And I would make trades and explain it by narrating it on the microphone.* "

Did anyone narrate their ancient algorithm presentation?

 Egyptian Multiplication is really adding.

These are the steps to multiply 23 x 10.

Write	Say
23	Thats 1 of it
23+23=46	Thats 2 of it
46+46=92	Thats 4 of it
92+92=184	Thats 8 of it
184+184=368	Thats 16 of it

 So you keep going down adding the number above on the left and squaring the number in the right column till you stop because the number in the right column is greater than the second number you multiply.

Here stop at 16 of it on the right because thats bigger than 10.
Then which numbers add up to 10? 8+2
Find the numbers that match on the left column. 46+ 184
46 + 184 add up to 230. That's the answer!

Multiply it our way to see!

category cards

EXAMINING VARIABLES IN ATTRIBUTE SETS

WHAT IS THIS INVESTIGATION ABOUT?

Our logical thinking is put to the test as we create our own attribute sets. Finding a way to determine the number of possible members in a set without drawing them all prepares us for algebra and higher level problem-solving, and our multimedia presentations provide us with new computer skills as well.

PLANNING FOR THE INVESTIGATION...

Paper	full sheets of paper, chart paper
Supplies	8" × 8" plastic bag for cards, colored marking pens for the teacher
Software	*The Multimedia Workshop*
Preparation	Cut 3" × 5" cards in half to make 3" × 2½" cards. Write the Attribute Summary shown below on chart paper.

before the investigation...

To warm up to attribute sets, show the students the Attribute Summary. **The category I have chosen is faces. I decided on three attributes—hair type, eye color, and expression. I made two or three options for each attribute. How many different faces can you draw that combine these attributes? Try it and see!**

ATTRIBUTE SUMMARY
Category: FACES

Hair Type: curly, straight
Eye Color: brown, blue, green
Expression: happy, sad

How many faces?

12 - in all!

INITIATING THE INVESTIGATION...

As we think about attribute sets, we use the terms *attributes* and *options*. First it was faces, now it is houses, finally it will be a topic of our own choosing!

▌ **Let's make an Attribute Summary for houses similar to the one you made for faces.** Tell the students the attributes are *Number of Stories, Number of Windows, Type of Path,* and *Type of Roof.* Ask the class to list two options for each attribute under the appropriate heading, such as one story, brick path, and peaked roof.

▶ The formula for finding the total number of members in an attribute set is: (number of options for attribute 1) x (number of options for attribute 2) x (number of options for attribute 3) and so on for as many attributes as there are in the set. In the houses attribute set, there are 2 x 2 x 2 x 2, or 16 members. Do not tell the students this rule. You will discuss it at the end of this investigation.

2 **Do you think you can draw all the possible combinations of houses in this set?** How many different unique houses will be in this set? Have pairs work together to draw as many different houses as possible without duplication on their note cards. When they finish, let them describe their cards and tell how many are in their set. **Each set is called an attribute set. It shows all the different combinations you can make with a certain set of characteristics.**

3 **I'd like for you to make a Category Card attribute set of your own.** As the students brainstorm sample categories, list them on the chalkboard. Try several of the categories with the class, having the students name attributes for the set and options for each attribute. On the chalkboard, write the Attribute Summary for each set.

4 Have pairs decide on a category, then write an Attribute Summary for it. **Think about what your set of Category Cards might look like**.

Possible Categories

- cars
- shirts
- planets
- alien creatures
- hot air balloons
- flowers

INTEGRATING SOFTWARE INTO THE INVESTIGATION...

The computer turns out to be a handy tool for making Category Cards. We're painting, but not with water colors!

Open **The Multimedia Workshop**
Select Paint Workshop
Create your illustration
Type in your text
Save **your illustration**

1 **Let's use the computer to make a set of cards.** Talk with the students about the various paint tools and let them demonstrate some of them. **How could you use the pencil or the brush to draw your Category Cards? Who can show us how to use the shape tools to draw a rectangle?**

2 **When you draw your pictures, make sure you space them far enough apart so they will be large enough when you print them.** See if students discover cutting and pasting as a strategy for using the same illustration, which they can then vary by only one attribute. Remind students to keep their drawings simple enough for others to interpret. Encourage the students to use patterns as an attribute.

Select Print

3 Students may need to save their cards in several files so that the drawings are not too close together. When they finish, they can print their files, color them, and cut them out to make cards.

ATTRIBUTE SUMMARY

Category - cars
type - coupe, wagon
no. doors - 2, 4
colors - blue, yellow

THINKING ABOUT THE INVESTIGATION...

Toward the end of the investigation, tell the class that mathematicians can determine the total number of unique members of an attribute set by looking at the number of options given for each attribute rather than by making drawings.

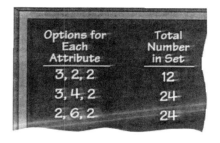

Options for Each Attribute	Total Number in Set
3, 2, 2	12
3, 4, 2	24
2, 6, 2	24

As pairs share the number of options for each of the attributes in their set of cards and the total number of cards in the set, keep a tally on the chalkboard. Let students look for patterns in the list that could be used to find the total number of members in each set.

- *Which sets have the same total number of members?*
- *What can we say about the number of attributes and options in each of those sets?*
- *What relationships do you see that affect the total number in the set?*

How did you feel about making your Category Cards using the Paint Workshop?

" *It was easy to make one car and then just change one thing at a time.* "

" *After we did the Category Cards on paper, I knew the total number of cars we would need to make so it was easier to keep track of the different ones.* "

What about the rest of you?

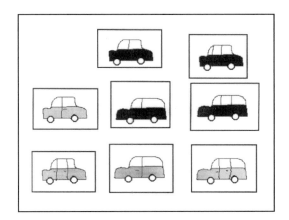

birdseed by the million
USING ESTIMATION TECHNIQUES TO COUNT ONE MILLION

WHAT IS THIS INVESTIGATION ABOUT?

Our sense of really large numbers is limited because few of us have had a chance to experience such numbers. We think about one million birdseeds, and then use those findings to help us figure out what one million of other familiar objects would be. Then we explain a million to the third-graders using our high-tech multimedia tools.

PLANNING FOR THE INVESTIGATION

Manipulatives Kit	*For the class:* 100 three-oz Portion Cups, 10 one-oz Portion Cups
Paper	full sheets of paper
Supplies	calculators
Software	*The Multimedia Workshop*
Preparation	You will need two 17-oz bags of small birdseed (preferably containing only one type of seed, such as millet).

before the investigation...

Show the class a bag full of some small object (rice, beans, breakfast cereal, or small metal washers). **Do you think there are more or less than a million objects in this bag? How could we find out?** Fill a three-oz cup with the objects. With the class, count the objects in the cup. **How many cups full of [this object] would you need to show about one million?** Explore different strategies with the students to come up with a solution.

INITIATING THE INVESTIGATION...

We explore the idea of a million using everyday objects. And we make a plan for showing one million birdseeds.

1 Hold up the bag of birdseed. ***Do you think there are more or less than a million seeds in this bag?*** Have students work together in groups of four to explore ideas. Open the bag of birdseed and set it out with 3-oz and 1-oz cups as the groups discuss the problem. ***Are there ways to use estimation to help you? How might you use the calculator to help you?***

2 Visit with groups that are having trouble getting started, and brainstorm with them for ideas on how the cups and calculator could be used. ***How could you use the cups to show what one million seeds would look like?***

> For your information, about 10,000 birdseeds fit in the 3-oz cup. This means 100 cups would hold about one million birdseeds. To actually display one million birdseeds, you would need twelve 16-oz bags of millet or 12 pounds of loose seed.

3 After the students come up with a plan to display one million seeds, have pairs make a drawing and write to tell about their thinking in response to the question, ***How many cups to hold one million _____?*** Students who complete their plans using the 3-oz cups may enjoy figuring out how many 1-oz cups it would take, and vice versa.

4 When the students complete their drawings of what one million birdseeds would look like, gather around to admire this view of such a large number.

INTEGRATING SOFTWARE INTO THE INVESTIGATION...

We make a video presentation to explain a million to the third-graders. It's an action-packed introduction to big numbers of small things.

Open *The Multimedia Workshop*
Select Paint Workshop
Create your illustrations
Save **your illustrations**

1 ***Let's start by making a picture. How do you think you could draw a picture on the computer?*** Encourage volunteers to explore the different paint tools. Students may also discover the time-saving copy, cut, and paste functions. Some students may want to finish the investigation here, and print their illustrations and color them as their finale. Other students are ready to make their illustrations into scenes as the next step to creating their presentation.

Select Video Workshop Scene Maker
Import **your illustration**
Select a background
Type in your text
Save **your scene**

2 ***Now let's put our illustration into a scene—all videos are just a series of scenes.*** Let a few students demonstrate how to add text and choose backgrounds. Suggest that they be creative to make their presentation exciting and colorful for the third-graders.

Open Libraries
Choose a photo
Import **the photo**
Select a background
Save **your scene**

3 ***How do you think you could insert a photo into a scene? Who can show how to add a wallpaper or picture background?***

We counted out seeds and put them into a cup. It took 336 seeds to fill it.

Then we tried to figer out how many cups it takes to get to 1,000,000. We used a calcalator. We did 1000000 ÷ 336 and got 2976.19.

Select Video Workshop Sequencer
Click on the first box on the
  video track
Import **your scene**
Select a transition
Place your transition
Save **your movie**
Click on the microphone icon
Record your narration
Save **your narration**

Select Video Workshop Sequencer
Click on the soundtrack
Import your narration
Save **your movie**

Open Playback
Click Save & Play
Select Auto Play

THINKING ABOUT THE INVESTIGATION...

4 *After you have made several scenes, open the Video Workshop Sequencer and put all your scenes together to make a video presentation.* Have students demonstrate how to place several scenes and transitions in the Sequencer. Placing transitions after each scene allows for smooth transitions.

5 *How could you add an explanation to the presentation? Think about what you would like to say to a third-grader about your scene.* Encourage students to explain their discoveries in a way a younger child would understand.

6 *Now we are ready to watch our creations! Voila!* Toward the end of the investigation, have pairs give their video presentations to pairs of third-graders. Tell them to ask the third-grade pairs one or two questions and report back their responses.

Gather the class after the presentations and discuss what they found out in their investigation.

- *Did you learn anything about a million that really surprised you?*
- *Can you think of anything that you have a million of at home?*

Would one million birdseeds fit inside my shoe?

 " No. Because your shoe is only about as big as three cups. That's not even a thousand!"

 " We might fit a million of something into your shoe, but it would be much smaller than birdseed. "

What are you thinking of that is small enough for a million of them to fit inside my shoe?

creating containers

INVESTIGATING CAPACITY AND LIQUID MEASURE

WHAT IS THIS INVESTIGATION ABOUT?

We identify equivalencies among ounces, cups, pints, and quarts. We make a chart showing the relationships among some of these different units of liquid measure on *The Cruncher*. This investigation is full of proportional thinking skills, as we grapple with equivalents, conversion, and other key measurement concepts.

PLANNING FOR THE INVESTIGATION...

Manipulatives Kit	*For the class:* Four-cup Measuring Cup *For each pair:* Vinyl Inch/Metric Ruler
Paper	full sheets of paper, 9" x 12" construction paper
Supplies	masking tape
Software	*The Cruncher*
Preparation	Make copies for each student of Liquid Measurement (page 42). Also have an empty half-gallon milk carton on hand to show the class.

before the investigation...

To prepare the class for their measuring investigation, have the students collect and bring in empty milk cartons with the tops cut off—half gallon, quart, pint, and half pint. Discuss the units of liquid measure on the containers.

INITIATING THE INVESTIGATION...

We take on calibration and equivalency in liquid measure. What are the units and what are some different names for the same amount?

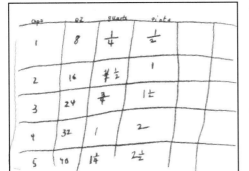

1. Hold up the four-cup measuring cup and have students tell as much as they can about it: what it's used for; what the lines, words, and numbers on the outside might be; and so on.

2. Point to the lines and tell the class that they are called *calibrations*. **Along with the units of measure and numbers beside them, they make it possible to use this container to measure many different amounts accurately.**

3. Hand out copies of the Liquid Measurement chart you have prepared. Discuss several of the calibrations with the class as the students look at their copy. Be sure to include those that have more than one unit of measure written beside them. **What can we say about a pint? quart?** Point to the 2-cup line on the chart. **How many ounces would this be? How about pints?**

4. **Now I'd like you to think about how you would make an Equivalent Measures Chart showing all the relationships you can among ounces, cups, pints, and quarts.** Have the students work together in pairs to make their chart as complete as possible. **Someone should be able to use your chart to look up equal measures.**

INTEGRATING SOFTWARE INTO THE INVESTIGATION...

We really give *The Cruncher* a workout as we put our equivalency charts together.

Open *The Cruncher*
Select New Spreadsheet

1 ***How could we make a measurement chart using* The Cruncher?** Review the elements in a spreadsheet: *formula bar, rows, columns,* and *cells.* Point them out on *The Cruncher.* **We'll start a spreadsheet together and then you can design your own.**

Select a cell
Type your title in the cell
Select Save
Select a cell
Type your data in the cell
Click on the check
Select Save

2 ***What title would you like to give our spreadsheet?*** Ask a volunteer to type a title suggested by the class. **What should you put into the columns?** Let volunteers type in several headings, such as Ounces and Cups, in the appropriate cells.

Select a cell
Type in an equal sign
Type in your formula
Click on the check
Select Save

3 ***After we fill in the data for the Ounces column, what is one relationship you would put on the spreadsheet to fill in the cells in the next column?*** Discuss the various formulas that *The Cruncher* will accept, such as =A1*B1 for multiplication and =B2/A1 for division. **Now let's try to figure out some equivalencies. How many cups is 8 ounces?** Show students how their formula for converting ounces to cups (number of ounces divided by 8) looks on the spreadsheet (=A4/8). Repeat the process down the column for cups until the students are comfortable with using the division formula. Then show students how they could use a multiplication formula to convert cups to ounces.

	A	B	C	D	E	F
1	**Equivalent Measures**					
2						
3	ounces	cups	pints	quarts		
4	8	1	0.5	0.25		
5	16	2	1	0.5		
6	24	3	1.5	0.75		
7	32	4	2	1		
8	40	5	2.5	1.25		
9						
10						
11						
12						
13						

Click Notes
Type in your notes
Select Option
Select Sticker Picker
Choose a sticker
Click OK
Move your sticker

Select File
Select Print

THINKING ABOUT THE INVESTIGATION...

4 *What could you say about the relationship between the different measuring units in the notes? Tell about your thinking, then use stickers to decorate your spreadsheet and notes.* Have a student type in some words in the notebook. Have another select a sticker and move it around on the spreadsheet or note.

5 Have pairs work at the computer to complete their spreadsheet, following the processes that the class used together. *Print your spreadsheet and notes, and color them if you'd like.*

Bring the class together to talk about the spreadsheets and equivalencies.

- *Can you tell me everything you know about a quart?*
- *Does your spreadsheet show how many ounces are in a quart? How does it show that?*

How did you use formulas in your spreadsheet?

" I made my first cell gallons so I went down to ounces. If I have one gallon I can see that I have 4 quarts by multiplying."

" I divided. I started with ounces, and then I divided cups by 8. So I got smaller and smaller numbers instead of bigger and bigger."

What were the formulas that you used?

	A	B	C	D
1		Liquid Measure		
2				
3	Quarts	pints	cups	oz.
4	1	=A4*2	=A4*4	=A4*32
5	2	=A5*2	=A5*4	=A5*32
6	3	=A6*2	=A6*4	=A6*32
7	4	=A7*2	=A7*4	=A7*32
8	6	=A8*2	=A8*4	=A8*32
9	5	=A9*2	=A9*4	=A9*32

boxes in boxes

APPLYING FRACTIONAL CONCEPTS AND MEASUREMENT IN THREE-DIMENSIONS

WHAT IS THIS INVESTIGATION ABOUT?

We agree to manage a school supply warehouse—we have to find out how many supplies each of our shipping boxes can hold. Once we know all the measurements, our knowledge of fractions, visual thinking, and calculation skills take over. The project is definitely a challenge, but we don't let ourselves get boxed in!

PLANNING FOR THE INVESTIGATION...

Manipulatives Kit *For each pair:*
Vinyl Inch/Metric Ruler

Paper full sheets of paper, chart paper

Supplies calculators

Software *The Cruncher*

Preparation Draw a ruler on the chalkboard. Gather one small, one medium, and one large (no bigger than 16" × 9" × 12") packing box. List the dimension of each on chart paper. Display 2 each of the following school supplies (still in packages or boxes): crayons, colored markers, tape, paper clips, staples, ream of paper, tissues, and a dictionary.

before the investigation...

Have the class identify the marks on their rulers that represent fractional parts of inches and then point to these marks on a ruler you've drawn on the chalkboard. Challenge the students to measure several different school supply packages to the nearest fraction of an inch. **How precise can you get?**

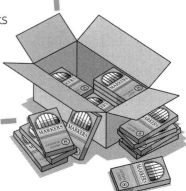

INITIATING THE INVESTIGATION...

We begin by figuring out packing plans for our school supply warehouse. How many supplies can we pack in each of the boxes?

1. Show the class the three sizes of shipping boxes and the school supply packages you've collected. **Imagine you're the packing managers at a school supply warehouse. Figure out how many of each supply you could pack into each size shipping box. Let's do one together.**

2. **How many of these marker boxes do you think we could pack into this smallest shipping box?** On chart paper, sketch and label the dimensions of your small shipping box. Measure the marker box, and record the dimensions with a similar sketch. **Make a copy of this small shipping box sketch on paper, then work with your partner to see if you can figure out how many marker boxes could be packed inside. Use sketches and calculations to verify your ideas.**

3. After pairs have had time to work, ask volunteers to come to the chalkboard to explain their thinking about the problem. **Which way were you packing the marker boxes? Would more fit if they would turned a different way?** Reach a group consensus on the number of marker boxes that can fit in the small shipping box.

4. **Work with your partner to make a chart telling how many of each school supply could be packed into each size of shipping box. Use paper for sketches and calculations, but record the final information on the chart.** Let students take turns measuring the school supply boxes, but use the shipping boxes for visual reference only. They can refer to the chart paper for shipping box dimensions.

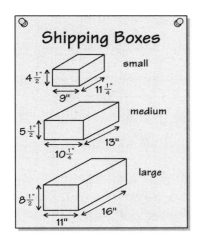

Shipping Boxes

small — $4\frac{1}{2}"$, $9"$, $11\frac{1}{4}"$

medium — $5\frac{1}{2}"$, $10\frac{1}{4}"$, $13"$

large — $8\frac{1}{2}"$, $11"$, $16"$

School Supplies	Small	Medium	Large
a box of Markers	7	9	32
Box of Crayons	9	13	48
paper	0	0	7
Dictionary	0	0	5
Box of paper Clips	32	56	136
Box of Staples	15	36	108
Box of tape	36	48	204
Box of Kleenex	0	0	5

INTEGRATING SOFTWARE INTO THE INVESTIGATION...

Our warehouse becomes computerized as we use *The Cruncher* to make our charts.

Open ***The Cruncher***
Select New Spreadsheet

1 *You can use the information you have on your chart to make a spreadsheet.* Before pairs begin, review the elements in a spreadsheet: *formula bar, rows, columns,* and *cells.* Point them out on *The Cruncher.* **Before you start, think about what you want to put into the columns and rows.**

Select a cell
Type your title in the cell
Select Save
Select a cell
Type your heading in the cell
Select Save

2 *What title would you like to give your chart? You could even make up your own clever company name.* Type in a title in a cell—Tons of School Supplies, for example. **What column headings could you enter in your spreadsheet?** Call on volunteers to enter column headings, such as Name of Supply, Small Box, and so on.

Select a cell
Type your data in the cell
Select Save

3 *How could we fill in the data for the Supply column? Let's fill in the numbers of boxes in the other columns.* Pick volunteers to show how to do this for several cells.

Select a cell
Type in an equal sign
Type in your formula
Click on the check
Select Save

4 *Your spreadsheet shows how many of each kind of supply each size box holds. How could we figure out how much to charge our customers for the supplies in them?* Make up prices for each school supply and write the prices on the chalkboard. **How can we get the computer to give us the total price of what is in each box?** Show students how a formula for multiplying the number of supplies times the price looks on the spreadsheet. For example, the 7 markers (in cell B4) cost 25¢ each (cell C4) so the formula for the total cost (in D4) =B4 * C4. Have students add columns for price and another for total cost for each of the box sizes. Use the formulas until the students are comfortable with them.

Click Notes
Type in your notes
Select Option
Select Sticker Picker
Choose a sticker
Click OK
Move your sticker

Select File
Select Print

THINKING ABOUT THE INVESTIGATION...

5 *What could you write in the notes that would tell about how you knew how many supplies would fit in each box? Or about how much the supplies in the box cost?* Click anywhere in the notebook window and ask a volunteer to type a short explanation. *Use the stickers to decorate your spreadsheet and notes.*

6 *Print your spreadsheet and notes. Add color to them if you'd like.*

Bring the class together to talk about their work and their computerized chart.

- *Did anyone use a calculator? How?*
- *Which supply and shipping box combinations were hardest to solve?*
- *How did you make your spreadsheet? What data is in your rows? columns?*

	A	B	C	D
1		Tons of School Supplies		
2				
3		small box	medium box	large box
4	markers	7	9	32
5	scissors	9	13	48
6	paper	0	0	7
7	calculators	36	48	204
8	dictionary	0	0	5
9				
10				
11				
12				
13				
14				

How does making a spreadsheet differ from making a chart on paper?

" *Well, I thought of the spreadsheet as a chart with rows and columns and did it like I would have on paper.* "

" *For figuring out the cost for each box the computer was useful. You have to be sure the information is in the correct cell, though.* "

What do the rest of you think?

	A	B	C	D	E
1		Tons of School Supplies			
2					
3		small box	prices	total cost	
4	markers	7	$0.25	=B4*$0.25	$0.75
5	scissors	9	$1.00	=B5*$1.00	$9.00
6	paper	2	$2.00	=B6*$2.00	$4.00
7	calculators	36	$20.00	=B7*$20.00	$720
8	dictionary	0	$5.00	=B8*$5.00	0
9					
10					
11					
12					
13					
14					

tessellation Art
CREATING TESSELLATION DESIGNS

WHAT IS THIS INVESTIGATION ABOUT?

As we explore tessellation, we hypothesize about a particular shape's ability to tessellate. Beyond the interesting mathematical discoveries that we make about tessellations, we learn that they are an intriguing art form as we create our own unique multimedia tessellations.

PLANNING FOR THE INVESTIGATION...

Manipulatives Kit *For each group of four:* Polygon Tiles and Definition Cards, Vinyl Inch/Metric Ruler

Paper full sheets of paper

Supplies scissors, tape, small plastic bags

Software *The Multimedia Workshop*

Preparation Put the tiles in bags according to their number so that all the same-numbered (matching) tiles are together in individual bags. Have thin pieces of cardboard or heavy card stock available for students to make their shapes.

before the investigation...

Give a bag of matching Polygon Tiles to each group of students. **If you had a puzzle made up of many pieces, all exactly the same shape and size, could you fit those pieces together in a way that you could completely fill a flat surface?** Demonstrate how this works on the chalkboard. Tell the students that when a shape can be repeated in a tiling pattern with no spaces between and the sum of the angles around any point is 360°, mathematicians say the shape *tessellates.* **Will your polygon shape tessellate? Try it and see!**

INITIATING THE INVESTIGATION...

By altering certain Polygon Tiles in a particular way, we create unique tessellating shapes. How amazing!

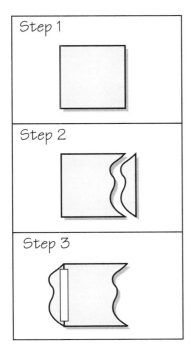

Step 1

Step 2

Step 3

1 *Before this investigation, you discovered that many of the Polygon Tiles tessellate. Do you think it is possible to alter some of the tiles in such a way that the new shapes will tessellate, too? Let's try that!*

2 Demonstrate the steps shown on the left to the students, having them follow along with tiles of their choice. *Select a Polygon Tile that you know will tessellate. Trace the tile onto cardboard and cut out the shape (Step 1). Cut a piece out of one side of the shape, making sure to hold on to the cut-out piece. Cut from corner to corner (Step 2). Place the cut-out piece on the opposite side of your original polygon shape and attach it with tape (Step 3).*

3 *Will your new shape tessellate? Try it out and see.* Ask the students to trace their new shapes several times onto blank sheets of paper to see if the new shapes will tessellate.

4 Have the students use the method outlined in Step 2 to make interesting shapes using other Polygon Tiles or shapes they cut out themselves. *Select one of your shapes to use in a tessellation design on the computer.*

▶ **Not all shapes that tessellate can be altered to create tesellating shapes. The shape must have at least two congruent sides. The key to creating a shape that will tessellate is in altering opposite sides in exactly the same way.**

will tessellate

will not tessellate

INTEGRATING SOFTWARE INTO THE INVESTIGATION...

Our imaginations run wild as we use our creativity and the computer to make some amazing designs.

Open **The Multimedia Workshop**
Select Paint Workshop
Create your illustration
Save **your illustration**

1. *Choose one of the shapes you have made. Does it remind you of anything—a face or an animal or an object ? Use your imagination! Make your shape into a tessellation design on the computer.* Remind students about the various paint tools that might be relevant to this investigation and let them demonstrate some of them: patterns, the brush, the spray can, the transmogrifier, and so on, to decorate each shape. *Make your design take on the personality you imagined.*

2. *How could you use the pencil tool to draw your shape? Does anyone know what the trick is to drawing a straight line?* For straight lines, hold down the Shift key while drawing. *The polygon tool draws geometric shapes with lots of sides. Who can show how it works?* Double-click the last point on the polygon tool to close the polygon.

3. *How could you copy and paste your shape without drawing it over again?*

4. Encourage the students to explore the Selection menu to invert, trace edges, flip horizontal, flip vertical, rotate 90°, and rotate by degrees.

Select your shape
Select Copy

5 Have students print their tessellation designs. Ask them to put four or five Polygon Tiles nearby, including the one they altered to create their design. Have the students take a classroom tour to admire the designs and figure out which tile was used to create each design.

THINKING ABOUT THE INVESTIGATION...

Gather the class together for a discussion of their work.

- *What did you discover about altering shapes to create new tessellating shapes?*
- *Why do you think it is possible to alter a shape in this way and still end up with a shape that will tessellate?*
- *Did you create any shapes that would not tessellate? Why do you think they wouldn't?*

What differences do you think you would notice if you were to make a tessellation on paper instead of the computer?

" *Laying down a pattern and just tracing it is easier than learning how to use all the options on the computer.* **"**

" *That's true, but you would have to repeat your shape and decoration on paper. With the computer, you just cut and paste. It's easy.* **"**

Any other ideas or comments?

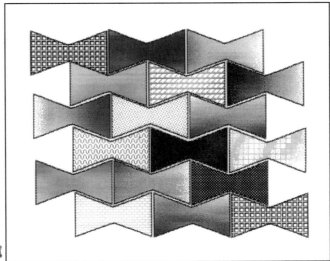

Number Systems expo
DEVELOPING AND TESTING ORIGINAL NUMBER SYSTEMS

WHAT IS THIS INVESTIGATION ABOUT?

We develop and refine a number system all our own. The thinking required in this investigation is especially challenging as we examine our number systems at every step of the creation process to see if they are complete, logical, and make sense to others. The culmination is a high-tech presentation of our number system using *The Multimedia Workshop*.

PLANNING FOR THE INVESTIGATION...

Paper	full sheets of paper, 10 × 10 grid paper (page 49)
Supplies	calculators
Software	*The Multimedia Workshop*
Preparation	Make multiple copies of the Chinese Stick and Roman Number System summaries (page 45). Make a copy for each pair of Inventing a Number System (page 46). Make at least five copies of each pair's Number System Summary sheets and stack them in their own pile in a central location.

before the investigation...

Have the students examine several number systems. Distribute the Chinese Stick and Roman Number System summaries. Ask them to fill in the missing numbers; use grid paper to make a 1 to 100 chart; solve the mystery numbers; write the current year, their address, and the year they were born; and write about how the system works. The goal here is understanding, not memorization.

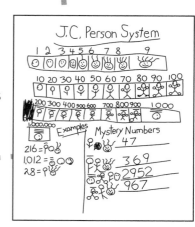

INITIATING THE INVESTIGATION...

As we invent our own number systems, creativity and the mathematics of it all come together.

Number System Summary

Roman

0	1	2	3	4	5	6	7	8	9
no zero	I	II	III	IV	V	VI	VII	VIII	IX

10	20	30	40	50	60	70	80	90
X	XX	XXX	XL	L	LX	LXX	LXXX	XC

100	200	300	400	500	600	700	800	900
C	CC	CCC	CD	D	DC	DCC	DCCC	CM

1,000	10,000	100,000	Million or Infinity
M	X̄	C̄	I∞I

Notes:
- When a symbol for a lesser number comes *before* the symbol for a greater number, subtract the lesser from the greater. IX = 9
- When a symbol with less value comes *after* one with greater value, add the lesser to the greater. XI = 11

Examples:
21 = XXI   240 = CCXL
63 = LXIII   1,490 = MCDXC

Mystery Numbers:
XLVII = _47_
CCCXCV = _395_
MDCCI = _1701_
CCXXII = _222_

1. ***Now that you have had some experience working with other number systems, let's try to put that knowledge to work.*** Tell the students that each pair's goal is to invent a new number system. The system may incorporate ideas or characteristics of systems explored previously, but should have some original elements. ***You'll try out each other's systems when you are done.***

2. Distribute the Inventing a Number System project guide and discuss the basic ideas with the class. Tell the students that they should complete one level before going to the next. ***As you're inventing your number system, you'll need to think about how the numerals in your system will work together to show larger numbers and what the numerals in your system will look like.***

3. As pairs work, rotate among them helping to clarify any questions they may have. When they have finished, make copies of their summaries.

4. Have pairs select a summary other than their own to explore. They should fill in the missing numbers and decipher the Mystery Numbers. They should write comments on the system. ***I'd like you to take the comments that were written and use those to revise your own number system for your presentation.***

> It is important for the students to challenge themselves at appropriate levels. Remind them that you're not interested in how quickly they are able to invent a number system, but in how well it appears that they've thought their ideas through. Often the first idea that comes to mind will simply serve as a springboard for more unique and interesting ideas.

INTEGRATING SOFTWARE INTO THE INVESTIGATION...

Our own number system presented on the computer... what an awesome thought, but we can do it!

Open **The Multimedia Workshop**
Select Paint Workshop
Create your illustration
Save **your illustration**

1 ***Let's think about ways to draw our number symbols on the computer.*** Discuss the various tools with the students and let them demonstrate some of them, such as the pencil or brush. ***There is a trick to drawing a straight line. Can anyone guess what it might be?*** (Hold down the Shift key while drawing to make straight lines.)

Select Video Workshop Scene
   Maker
Import **your illustration**
Open Libraries
Choose Clip Art **or** Photographs
Import **your illustration**
Save **your scene**

2 ***All videos are just a series of scenes.*** Tell the students they can add as many new scenes as they want to describe their number system using illustrations they've created in the Paint Workshop or others available in the Libraries: photos, clip art and so on. ***Be as creative as you can. How do you think you could insert a photo related to your number system into the scene?***

Click the microphone icon
Select Record
Record your narration
Save **your narration**

3 Ask the students to think about what kind of sound they'd like to go with their scene. ***What could you say about your scene?*** Encourage students to narrate an explanation of their systems in ways that their classmates will understand. Other students may be more comfortable just adding music or sound from the Libraries during the sequencing of their presentation.

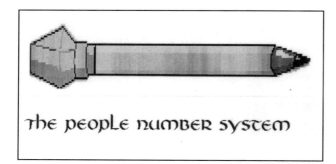

Select Video Workshop Sequencer
Click on the first box on the video track
Import **your scene**
Select a transition
Place your transition
Save **your movie**

Click on the soundtrack
Open Libraries
Open Sound
Select some sound or music
Select your narration
Save **your movie**

Open Playback
Click Save & Play
Select Auto Play

THINKING ABOUT THE INVESTIGATION...

4 *After you have made several scenes, you can put them together to make a video presentation. How will you decide the order for your scenes?* Have students demonstrate how to place several scenes and transitions in the Video Workshop Sequencer.

5 *How could you add sound and music to the presentation?* Students can import the files that have the messages they recorded or the music they would like in their videos.

6 *Now we are ready to watch our creations!* As the students finish their movies, have each pair give their presentation to the class.

Gather the class after all the videos have been viewed and discuss the number systems.

- *Which systems were easy to understand? Which were difficult?*
- *Were any systems similar to each other? How were they alike?*

What changes were suggested that made your system better?

" *Someone noticed that a circle can be either a zero or ten.* "

" *So we decided to change zero to another symbol. We made the change at the computer.* "

Any other changes on systems?

examples

211 = ♀ | ○ ⊙

1021 = ⌐⊔⌐ | ♀ ⊙

MYSTERY NUMBERS

⊙ _____

♀ | _____

⌐⊔⌐ | ⌐⊔⌐ ☺ _____

predictions

USING SAMPLING TO MAKE PREDICTIONS

WHAT IS THIS INVESTIGATION ABOUT?

We learn that we can predict the chances of an event through a technique called *sampling*. Although we can't be absolutely sure about actual numbers, the information from sampling helps us make generalizations and predictions in situations where specific data are unknown or hard to acquire. Organizing and graphing our results on the computer expands the ways we organize our data.

PLANNING FOR THE INVESTIGATION...

Manipulatives Kit	*For each group of four:* 100 Rainbow Cubes in assorted colors
Paper	full sheets of paper, eighth sheets of paper
Supplies	lunch sacks (1 for each group of four)
Software	*The Cruncher*
Preparation	Provide students with the total number of students in the school. Cut several eighth sheets of paper in half to make 16 slips of paper from each sheet.

before the investigation...

Put 100 Rainbow Cubes of 4 different colors in paper bags for each group of four. Tell students that there are 100 cubes in 4 colors in their bag. **How many of each color are there?** Have students write down their predictions. Tell them that mathematicians use a technique called *sampling* to make predictions involving *unknowns*. Have the groups take 10 cubes out of their bag and record the results. Then have them take out 20 cubes, then 50. Open the bags. Discuss the predictions and results.

INITIATING THE INVESTIGATION...

We use sampling as a technique to help determine how many of each type of drink to buy for an all-school party. Are our guests satisfied with our predictions?

1 *Let's suppose that we have to decide what drinks to get for a party for the whole school. We can buy only four kinds of drinks—which four kinds should we get?* Brainstorm a list of drinks and let the class choose four. Tell the class the number of students in your school. **How many of each drink should we buy?**

> The concept of **proportion**—the acceptance that if 7 out of 10 want soda, then 70 out of 100 will want soda, is something that students must come to an understanding of on their own. Investigations such as this one provide the opportunities to help the students develop this ability.

2 *We can't ask every student what they want, but we can afford to buy only one drink for each student. Would sampling our class help us make our decision? Let's see.* Have students write their drink preferences on slips of paper. Put all the slips in a bag and let a student draw from the bag, keeping a tally of the results on the chalkboard. As they draw 10 slips, then half, and finally all of them, ask these questions. **Can we decide on the number of each drink to buy from this information? Can we predict the most popular drink? least popular? If we knew our preferences were representative of the whole school, how many of each drink would we need to buy?**

3 *Before we look at the results, I'd like you to write your predictions. What are you basing your predictions on?* Challenge the students to gather more data to improve their predictions, such as interviewing students from other classes at recess. Tally the data from the other classrooms on the chalkboard.

INTEGRATING SOFTWARE INTO THE INVESTIGATION...

Now we're ready to put the data into a spreadsheet and view the results on graphs. They're other ways of comparing our results to our predictions.

1 *Let's think about how you and your partner could display the results and predictions on the computer. We'll create a spreadsheet together, then you and your partner can make your own.* Review the elements in a spreadsheet: formula bar, rows, columns, and cells.

Open *The Cruncher*
Select New Spreadsheet
Select a cell
Type your title in the cell
Select Save
Select a cell
Type your heading in the cell
Select Save

2 *What could you title it?* Have a volunteer type in a title such as School Party. *What column headings could we enter for this spreadsheet?* Have a volunteer type in the column headings, such as Names of Drinks, How Many?, and Predictions.

Select a cell
Type your data in the cell
Select Save

3 *We've made the first column heading "Names of Drinks." What will we put in the cells under that heading?* Have volunteers type in the drink names in the appropriate cells. *What other column headings do we need?* Under How Many? have students type in the numbers.

Select a cell
Select Options
Select Functions
Choose Sum
Drag the cursor through the cells you choose
Click on the check
Select Save

4 Remind students that the Sum function adds up the numbers in a range of cells. *Is there any way to use this function on your spreadsheet to show the total number of drinks?* Use Sum on each cell in one column to demonstrate the use of this function. Encourage volunteers to try the procedure until students are comfortable with the process.

	A	B	C
1		Our Favorite Drinks	
2			
3	drink	how much	predicted
4	Lemonade	9	3
5	cola	13	15
6	cherry	1	1
7	ginger ale	8	10
8	water	1	3
9			
10	total	=SUM(B4:B8)	=SUM(C4:C8)
11			

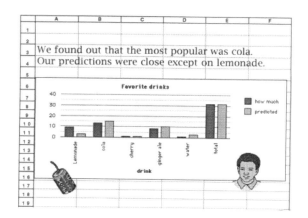

Select the cells for the chart
Select Options
Select Chart
Click on the type of chart
Type in the title
Label the X and Y axes
Click OK

Click Notes
Type in your notes
Select Option
Select Sticker Picker
Choose a sticker
Click OK
Move your sticker

Select File
Select Print

THINKING ABOUT THE INVESTIGATION...

5 Discuss various kinds of graphs with the students. *What kind of graph would work well with this problem?* Have students try several graphs to see which ones provide the most useful information.

6 *Let's tell about what you learned about sampling in the notes.* Have a student type in several sentences to demonstrate. *Decorate your spreadsheet and notebook with stickers.*

7 Have pairs work at the computer to design a spreadsheet similar to the one the class started. *Remember to print your spreadsheet and notes.* Give students time to explore the software options.

Toward the end of the investigation, compare the results to the predictions and discuss the variety of spreadsheets and graphs the students made to show the comparison.

- *How close were your predictions?*
- *Is sampling helpful in making a prediction? Why or why not? Can we predict exact results by sampling?*

What can you say about the results by looking at your spreadsheet and graph?

" *Well, I could see from my spreadsheet that the most popular drink was soda.* "

" *And the graph showed the same thing, too. Soda was the longest bar.* "

" *We did a circle graph. It's called a* pie graph on The Cruncher. *The biggest piece of our "pie" was soda, too.* "

Anyone use another type of graph to see the results?

GROWING SHAPES EXPLORATIONS

1. What patterns do you discover when you build growing triangles? Make a recording that shows what you found and explain the pattern. Make grid paper models or use a chart similar to the one you made with the class.

2. Try the exploration above using a different Pattern Block shape.

3. Compare the patterns you find for different Growing Shapes. How are the patterns alike? different? Report your findings.

4. How far can you go with a Growing Shapes pattern? Pick a shape and see what happens. Report on the patterns using words, sketches, or numbers. Predict as much as you can about the 10th, 50th, and 100th shape in the series. Use a calculator in this exploration if you'd like.

- -

LIQUID MEASUREMENT

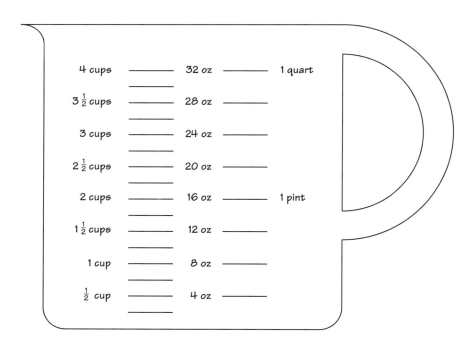

4 cups	32 oz	1 quart
3 ½ cups	28 oz	
3 cups	24 oz	
2 ½ cups	20 oz	
2 cups	16 oz	1 pint
1 ½ cups	12 oz	
1 cup	8 oz	
½ cup	4 oz	

RUSSIAN PEASANT MULTIPLICATION 21×19

1. Make two columns on your paper. Label the first column "Halving" and the second column "Doubling." Write the first number under "Halving" and the second number under "Doubling."

2. Halve the first number until you reach 1, writing the answer each time in the first column. Disregard any remainders.

3. Double the second number, writing the answer each time in the second column. Do this the same number of times it took you to halve the first number.

4. Draw a line through each row that has an even number in the "Halving" column.

5. Add the numbers in the "Doubling" column that do not have a line drawn through them as in the example below:

Halving	Doubling	
21 ×	19	
10	38	("Halving" number is even.)
5	76	
2	152	("Halving" number is even.)
1	304	

Add: 19 + 76 + 304 = 399

21 × 19 = 399

LATTICE MULTIPLICATION 455×34

• Draw a rectangle with 455 across the top and 34 down the right side.

• Draw diagonal lines from the upper right to the lower left. Write in the multiplication facts.

• Figure out the sum of the diagonals, starting at the far right.

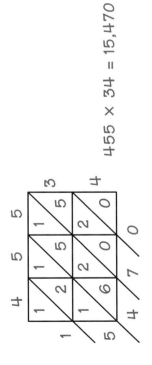

455 × 34 = 15,470

EGYPTIAN MULTIPLICATION
69x19

1. Write the first number you are multiplying in the first column. Say to yourself, "That's 1 of it." Write this in the second column.

2. Add the first number to itself and write the equation in the first column. Say to yourself, "That's 2 of them." Write this in the second column.

3. Add the sum to itself and write the equation in the first column. Say to yourself, "That's 4 of them." Write this in the second column.

4. Add the sum to itself and write the equation in the first column. Say to yourself, "That's 8 of them." Write this in the second column.

5. Continue this pattern (1, 2, 4, 8, 16, 32, 64, 128,...) until you say to yourself a number that is greater than the second number you are multiplying. In the example, this number is 32 because 32 is greater than 19.

69	That's 1 of it.
69 + 69 = 138	That's 2 of them.
138 + 138 = 276	That's 4 of them.
276 + 276 = 552	That's 8 of them.
552 + 552 = 1104	That's 16 of them.
1104 + 1104 = 2208	That's 32 of them.

6. Now, find a way to add the numbers you've been writing in the second column so that the sum is exactly the second number you are multiplying, which in this example is 19.

$$16 + 2 + 1 = 19$$

7. Find the corresponding sums in the first column and add them together.

$$1104 + 138 + 69 = 1311$$

$$69 \times 19 = 1311$$

0	1	2	3	4	5	6	7	8	9
0	I	II	III	IIII	IIIII	T	TT		

10	20	30	40	50	60	70	80	90
—		III		≡	T	T̄		

100	200	300	400	500	600	700	800	900
	II			IIIII	T		III	

1,000	2,000
—	=

Notes: Sticks alternate direction as place value changes.

Thousands	Hundreds	Tens	One
I	I	I	I

Examples:

11 = — I

23 = = III

475 = IIII T̄ IIII

1,957 = — TTT ≡ TT

11,399 = I— III ≡ III

Mystery Numbers:

≡ III = _____

I T̄ TTT = _____

II ≡ = = _____

T̄ 0 IIII = = _____

0	1	2	3	4	5	6	7	8	9
no zero	I	II	III	IV	V	VI	VII		IX

10	20	30	40	50	60	70	80	90
X	XX		XL	L	LX			XC

100	200	300	400	500	600	700	800	900
C			CD	D	DC			CM

1,000	10,000	100,000
M	$\overline{\text{X}}$	$\overline{\text{C}}$

Million or Infinity

∞

Notes:
- When a symbol for a lesser number comes *before* the symbol for a greater number, subtract the lesser from the greater. IX = 9
- When a symbol with less value comes *after* one with greater value, add the lesser to the greater. XI = 11

Examples:

21 = XXI   240 = CCXL

63 = LXIII   1409 = MCDIX

Mystery Numbers:

XLVII = _____

CCCXCV = _____

MDCCI = _____

CCXXII = _____

INVENTING A NUMBER SYSTEM

Level 1: Design Your System

Invent a number system.

1. How will it work?

2. How will your numerals look?

3. How will your numerals work together to show bigger numbers?

Level 2: Test and Revise Your System

Test your system. Make changes, where necessary, to make your system better.

1. Is your system understandable? (If it's too complicated for anyone to figure out it's not useful.)

2. Can anyone write any number with your system?

3. Are there certain numbers in your system that are of key importance?

4. How high does your system go?

5. Is there one or are there several ways to write each number?

Level 3: Write a Number System Summary

Make a Number System Summary sheet for your system like the ones you used to explore the ancient number systems.

1. Think of a name for your system.

2. Make a chart that shows how to write some of the key numerals in your system. Leave some numbers out for your classmates to complete later.

3. Include any special notes you need to help explain any complicated parts of your system.

4. Write a few Mystery Numbers in your system for your classmates to decode later.

5. Write your name and your partner's name on the back of your summary sheet. For now, your systems should be anonymous.

1-INCH GRID

TRIANGLE GRID